寻狗总动员

【美】罗瑞·哈斯金丝·郝兰◎著

【美】艾米·乌莫尔◎绘

范晓星◎译

天津出版传媒集团

新蕾出版社

送给真正的乔丹。谢谢你给了我创作这个故事的灵感。

——罗瑞·哈斯金丝·郝兰

送给我们心爱的宠物：步步、小石头、弗林特和珠珠。

——艾米·乌莫尔

图书在版编目 (CIP) 数据

寻狗总动员/(美)郝兰(Houran,L.H.) 著;(美)
乌莫尔(Wummer,A.)绘;范晓星译.-- 天津:新蕾出
版社,2016.6(2024.12 重印)
(数学帮帮忙·互动版)
书名原文：A Thousand Theos
ISBN 978-7-5307-6399-5

Ⅰ.①寻… Ⅱ.①郝…②乌…③范… Ⅲ.①数学–
儿童读物Ⅳ.①O1–49

中国版本图书馆 CIP 数据核字(2016)第 078688 号

A Thousand Theos by Lori Haskins Houran; illustrated by Amy Wummer. Text copyright © 2015 by Lori Haskins Houran. Illustrations copyright © 2015 by Amy Wummer. All rights reserved, including the right of reproduction in whole or in part in any form. This edition published by arrangement with Kane Press, Inc. New York, NY, represented by The ChoiceMaker Korea Co.
Simplified Chinese translation copyright © 2016 by New Buds Publishing House (Tianjin) Limited Company
ALL RIGHTS RESERVED
本书中文简体版专有出版权经由中华版权代理中心授予新蕾出版社(天津)有限公司。未经许可,不得以任何方式复制或抄袭本书的任何部分。
津图登字：02–2015–224

出版发行　天津出版传媒集团
　　　　　新蕾出版社
http://www.newbuds.com.cn
地　　址:天津市和平区西康路 35 号(300051)
出 版 人:马玉秀
电　　话:总编办 (022)23332422
　　　　　发行部 (022)23332679　23332351
传　　真:(022)23332422
经　　销:全国新华书店
印　　刷:天津新华印务有限公司
开　　本:787mm×1092mm　1/16
印　　张:3
版　　次:2016 年 6 月第 1 版　2024 年 12 月第 20 次印刷
定　　价:12.00 元

无处不在的数学

资深编辑　卢　江

　　人们常说"兴趣是最好的老师"，有了兴趣，学习就会变得轻松愉快。数学对于孩子来说或许有些难，因为比起语文，数学显得枯燥、抽象，不容易理解，孩子往往不那么喜欢。可许多家长都知道，学数学对于孩子的成长和今后的生活有多么重要。不仅数学知识很有用，学习数学过程中获得的数学思想和方法更会影响孩子的一生，因为数学素养是构成人基本素质的一个重要因素。但是，怎样才能让孩子对数学产生兴趣呢？怎样才能激发他们兴致勃勃地去探索数学问题呢？我认为，让孩子读些有趣的书或许是不错的选择。读了这套"数学帮帮忙"，我立刻产生了想把它们推荐给教师和家长朋友们的愿望，因为这真是一套会让孩子爱上数学的好书！

　　这套有趣的图书从美国引进，原出版者是美国资深教育专家。每本书讲述一个孩子们生活中的故事，由故事中出现的问题自然地引入一个数学知识，然后通过运用数学知识解决问题。比如，从帮助外婆整理散落的纽扣引出分类，从为小狗记录藏骨头的地点引出空间方位等等。故事素材全部来源于孩子们的真实生活,不是童话,不是幻想,而是鲜活的生活实例。正是这些发生在孩子身边的故事,让孩子们懂得,数学无处不在并且非常有用;这些鲜活的实例也使得抽象的概念更易于理解,更容易激发孩子学习数学的兴趣,让他们逐渐爱上数学。这样的教育思想和方法与我国近年来提倡的数学教育理念是十分吻合的!

这是一套适合5~8岁孩子阅读的书,书中的有趣情节和生动的插画可以将抽象的数学问题直观化、形象化,为孩子的思维活动提供具体形象的支持。如果亲子共读的话,家长可以带领孩子推测情节的发展,探讨解决难题的办法,让孩子在愉悦的氛围中学到知识和方法。

值得教师和家长朋友们注意的是,在每本书的后面,出版者还加入了"互动课堂"及"互动练习",一方面通过一些精心设计的活动让孩子巩固新学到的数学知识,进一步体会知识的含义和实际应用;另一方面帮助家长指导孩子阅读,体会故事中数学之外的道理,逐步提升孩子的阅读理解能力。

我相信孩子读过这套书后一定会明白,原来,数学不是烦恼,不是包袱,数学真能帮大忙!

"乔丹姐姐,你看见我们家的狗了吗?"

乔丹低头看看邻居家的小弟弟本尼。他平时
总是活蹦乱跳的,自己就像一只小狗!可今天他
怎么了?

"我没见到呀。"乔丹说道,"它丢了吗?"

本尼点点头,"你看。"

顺着本尼手指的方向,乔丹看到本尼的妈妈正在往前门上贴 1 张纸。

寻狗启事

它的名字叫西奥。

它非常温柔。
它的家在橡树大街
36号2单元。
它喜欢吃花生酱。
如果你找到了它，
请拨打：
555-1238

5

"我们现在就去找它好不好？"本尼央求妈妈。

"对不起，宝贝，我们要出门了。"妈妈说，"我保证，一定有人能看到你写的寻狗启事，而且会帮助咱们找到西奥。"

"只有这 1 张小纸条儿。"本尼带着哭腔说。

"我再写1张吧。"乔丹自告奋勇地说，"我去训练的时候把它贴到足球场上。"

　　"那太好啦！"本尼的妈妈说，"哦，公交车来了。快点儿，本尼。"

　　"别担心。"乔丹对本尼说，"我们会找到西奥的！"

乔丹跑上楼。

她找出水彩笔，把本尼的寻狗启事抄了一遍。她还在四角加上了红色的星星，让这张纸看起来更显眼。

要是我能再多抄几张就好了，乔丹想。但不管怎样，2张肯定比1张效果好。

寻狗启事

它的名字叫西奥。
它非常温柔。
它的家在橡树大街
36号2单元。
它喜欢吃花生酱。
如果你找到了它，
请拨打：
555-1238

本尼

↓

乔丹

1+1=2

乔丹贴广告的时候，可拉和卡尔骑车经过。

"发生什么事了？"可拉问。

"多可爱的小狗哇！"卡尔说。

乔丹把本尼丢了小狗的事告诉了他们。

"本尼担心 1 张寻狗启事不够，所以我就又做了
1 张。"乔丹说。

"可怜的小家伙！"可拉说，"那我也帮他做1张吧！"

"我也要做！"卡尔说，"这样就有4张寻狗启事了，数量翻倍了。"

嗯，乔丹心想，翻倍。她有了一个好主意。

本尼

↓

乔丹

可拉　　　卡尔

2+2=4

11

"你们可不可以每人再找2个朋友,让他们也都各抄1张寻狗启事呢?"乔丹问,"这样数字就又翻倍了,就能有8张了。"

　　"好的!"可拉说。

　　"我们这就去!"卡尔说。

乔丹很兴奋。8 张寻狗启事，这真的很不错！总会有人能看见其中 1 张，并且帮忙找到小狗的。到时候，本尼会多开心哪！

　　可拉和卡尔马上就抄好了寻狗启事。可拉把启事贴到了轮滑场门口，她在那里遇到了马克和艾比。他俩也愿意加入进来，一起抄写寻狗启事。

卡尔把他的启事贴到了图书馆的通告栏里。他把事情经过告诉了伊万和莉娜。这两个人也迫不及待地抄写起来。

很快，8张寻狗启事就贴在了小镇的不同地方。

$$4+4=8$$

可这还没有结束。每个抄写寻狗启事的孩子
又分头去邀请 2 个孩子来一起抄启事。
马克找到了邻居家的尼克和安迪。

本尼

乔丹

可拉

卡尔

马克　　　　艾比　　　　伊万　　　　莉娜

尼克　安迪　瑞蕾　山姆　泰勒　布莱特　凯瑞　菲奥

$$8 + 8 = 16$$

艾比询问了
队友瑞蕾和山姆。

伊万打电话给表哥
泰勒和布莱特。

莉娜请好朋友凯瑞
和菲奥娜来帮忙。

一传十，十传百。寻狗启事的数量不断地翻倍。

到了午餐的时候，海盗比萨饼屋、快乐玩具店和优质鲜花坊外都贴上了寻狗启事。

$$16 + 16 = 32$$
$$32 + 32 = 64$$
$$64 + 64 = 128$$

到了晚餐的时候，碰碰保龄球馆、麦克自行车行和小书房书店外也都贴上了寻狗启事。

可是仍旧没有找到西奥……

寻狗启事的数量在继续翻倍,镇上的每个孩子都抄了1张!

　　乔丹简直不敢相信,街上到处都能看到西奥的小脸。一定会有人找到它的,对不对?

$$128 + 128 = 256$$
$$256 + 256 = 512$$
$$512 + 512 = 1024$$

"乔丹！乔丹！"本尼一边喊，一边沿着人行道跑来，"看哪，到处都是西奥！有100张吧！"

"我觉得差不多有1000张了。"本尼的妈妈说。

"1000只西奥！"本尼高兴地喊道，"都是你抄的吗？"

乔丹摇摇头。

"我只抄了 1 张。然后,我的 2 个朋友每人抄了 1 张。他们各自又请 2 个朋友每人抄了 1 张,朋友的朋友又请朋友抄……就这样,数量翻倍又翻倍,神速!"

"哇！"本尼欢呼道。

不过，他的笑容很快就消失了。

"可……我们还是没有找到西奥。"

本尼坐在家门口的台阶上。妈妈和乔丹陪在他的
身边。

丁零！丁零！丁零！

本尼不用抬头就知道是冰激凌车来了。乔丹看到卖冰激凌的伯伯把车停在了他们的楼前。

"嗨！孩子们！"卖冰激凌的伯伯说，"本来我想打个电话，可最终还是决定顺路送过来。这个小家伙是你的吗？"他抱起一只扭来扭去的棕色小狗问道。

"西奥！"本尼喊了出来。

冰激凌口味

● 香草
● 巧克力
● 花生酱
● 草莓
● 樱桃香草
● 什锦水果

　　小狗从伯伯的怀里跳下来，直奔本尼。本尼紧紧地
抱住了它。

　　"您在哪儿找到它的？"本尼问。

　　"在小镇的那头啦！我看到了满大街的寻狗启事，
一下子就认出这小家伙是西奥了。不过，我还是请它吃
了一口花生酱冰激凌来确认了一下。"

"太谢谢您了！"本尼说。

"别客气！"卖冰激凌的伯伯说，"你们想吃冰激凌吗？"

"好的，谢谢！"本尼挑了花生酱冰激凌，好跟西奥一起吃。乔丹选了撒糖粒儿的樱桃香草冰激凌。

　　卖冰激凌的伯伯按了几声喇叭，开心地把冰
激凌车开走了。

　　"谢谢您！"本尼在车后高声喊道。

　　"汪！汪！"西奥也跟着叫起来。

"也要谢谢你呀，乔丹。"本尼的妈妈说，"我们该怎么感谢所有帮我们抄寻狗启事的人呢？"

"这个简单！"乔丹笑眯眯地说，"只要感谢 1 个人，然后让这个人去传话给另外 2 个人就好啦！数量翻倍又翻倍，很快就可以把感谢的话传给 1000 个人啦！"

翻 倍 表

乔丹说得对。数量翻倍又翻倍，神速！从 1 开始，连续翻倍，只要 10 次，就可以超过 1000 了。

$1 + 1 = 2$

$2 + 2 = 4$

$4 + 4 = 8$

$8 + 8 = 16$

$16 + 16 = 32$

$32 + 32 = 64$

$64 + 64 = 128$

$128 + 128 = 256$

$256 + 256 = 512$

$512 + 512 = 1024$

亲爱的家长朋友，请您和孩子一起完成下面这些内容，会有更大的收获哟！

提高阅读能力

- 阅读封面，包括书名、作者等信息。读一下封面上的寻狗启事。你觉得这会是一个什么样的故事？
- 读过故事后，请看第 5 页。你觉得本尼遇到了什么难题？如果你的东西丢了或者找不到了，你会怎么办？你会到处寻找吗？你会告诉别人吗？本尼的妈妈用什么办法帮本尼找小狗？
- 请再次阅读第 12 页。说一说乔丹用了什么办法？翻倍是怎么回事？
- 请看第 9、11、15、16、18、20 页的算式，理解翻倍的概念。

巩固数学概念

- 请看第 22 页。本尼说"1000 只西奥"是什么意思？在故事中，最后一共有多少张寻狗启事？
- 想一想，如果本尼一开始做了 3 张寻狗启事，乔丹也抄了 3 张寻狗启事，那么 3+3=6。现在用翻倍的方法，几次可以达到 1000 张？这样是不是比故事里翻倍的次数少？

生活中的数学

- 在便笺上分别写下数字 1~8，做成数字卡片，放进一顶帽子或者一个纸袋里。请孩子选两个数字，再请他预测一下，如果要通过翻倍的方法达到 1000，哪个数字所需的翻倍次数最少？之后，请孩子用纸和笔计算一下，看看他的预测是否正确。

下图中, 每个→代表
翻倍 1 次, 你能在□中填
出每次翻倍后的得数吗?

3→□→□→□→□

现在从 5 开始翻倍,
你能在□中填出每次翻
倍后的得数吗?

5→□→□→□→□→□

乔丹一边品尝着美味的冰激凌，一边和卖冰激凌的伯伯聊天。看一看他们的聊天内容，计算一下，乔丹的年龄要翻倍几次，才能和卖冰激凌的伯伯的年龄一样？

4 翻倍 6 次和 6 翻倍 4 次,哪个的得数更大?

这可难不倒我!

1 张纸,如果对折 4 次,一共可以分成多少份? 先试着猜一猜,然后找 1 张纸试一下吧!

把1根绳子对折后剪开，然后再对折、剪开，剪5次后，这根绳子一共被剪成了多少段？

卡尔和乔丹商定,从这个月开始,他俩要按照各自的方法存钱。卡尔每个月存 10 元。乔丹第 1 个月存 2 元,第 2 个月存 4 元,第 3 个月存 8 元,以此类推。半年后,谁存的钱比较多?

10+10+10+…

2+4+8+…

互动练习 1：

(1) 3 → 6 → 12 → 24 → 48

(2) 5 → 10 → 20 → 40 → 80 → 160

互动练习 2：

3 次。

互动练习 3：

4 翻倍 6 次的得数更大。

互动练习 4：

一共可以分成 16 份。

互动练习 5：

一共被剪成了 32 段。

互动练习 6：

半年后，乔丹存的钱比较多。

互动练习 7：

19，28

A Thousand Theos

"Jordan, have you seen my puppy?"

Jordan looked down at her neighbor Benny. He was usually bouncy and happy—kind of like a puppy himself! But not today.

"I haven't seen him," said Jordan. "Is he lost?"

Benny nodded. "See?"

Jordan read the sign Benny's mom was taping to the front door.

"Can't we look for him now?" Benny begged his mom.

"I'm so sorry, honey—we have to go," she said. "But I bet someone will see your sign and find him."

"It's just one little sign," said Benny in a shaky voice.

"I'll make another one," Jordan offered. "I can hang it up at the soccer field on my way to practice."

"That would be great!" said Benny's mom. "Oh, here's our bus. Come on, Benny."

"Don't worry," Jordan told him. "We'll find Theo!"

Jordan ran upstairs.

She took out her markers and copies Benny's sign. She added bright red stars in the corners to make it stand out.

I wish I could do more to help, she thought. Still, two signs were twice as good as one.

$1+1=2$

Jordan was putting up her sign when Cora and Carl rode by on their bikes.

"What's up?" asked Cora.

"Cute dog!" said Carl.

Jordan told them about Benny's lost puppy.

"Benny was worried that one sign wasn't enough. So I made a second one," Jordan explained.

"Poor little guy!" said Cora. "I'll make a sign."

"Me too," said Carl. "That will double the signs to four."

Hmm, thought Jordan. Double. That gave her an idea.

$2+2=4$

"Do you think you could each get two more friends to make signs?" asked Jordan. "That would double the number again—to eight."

"Cool!" said Cora.

"We're on it!" said Carl.

Jordan felt much better. Eight signs—that was pretty good! Maybe somebody would see one and find Theo. Benny would be so happy!

Cora and Carl made their signs right away. Cora tacked hers up at the skateboard park, where she ran into Mack and Abby. They wanted to make signs too.

Carl stapled his sign on the library bulletin board. He told Evan and Leena (very quietly!) what was going on. They couldn't wait to make signs of their own.

Soon there were eight Lost Dog signs hanging up around town.

$4+4=8$

But it didn't stop there. Everyone who made a sign asked two more kids to make one.

Mack asked his neighbors Nick and Andy.

8+8=16

Abby asked her teammates Riley and Sam.

Evan asked his cousins Tyler and Brett.

Leena asked her best friends, Carrie and Fiona.

The word kept spreading. The signs kept doubling!

By lunchtime, there were signs at Pirate Pizza, Joy's Toys, and The Awesome Blossom.

16+16=32

32+32=64

64+64=128

By dinnertime, there were signs at Bowl-a-Bunch, Mike's Bikes, and The Book Nook.

And still ...

... the signs kept doubling, until every kid in town had made one!

Jordan couldn't believe it. Theo's face was everywhere! Someone had to find him now, didn't they?

128+128=256

256+256=512

512+512=1,024

"Jordan! Jordan!" called Benny, running up the sidewalk. "Look at all the Theos! There must be a hundred of them!"

"I think it's more like a thousand," said his mom.

"A thousand Theos!" Benny yelped.

"Did you make them all?"

Jordan shook her head.

"I only made one. Then two friends made them. They each asked two friends, and they each asked two friends, and ... well, it turns out doubling works fast!"

"Wow!" said Benny.

Then his smile faded.

"But ... the real Theo is still gone."

Benny sat down on the steps. His mom and Jordan sat beside him.

DING! DING! DING!

Benny didn't even look up at the sound of the ice cream truck. Jordan watched it pull in front of their building.

"Hi there," the ice cream man said. "I was going to call, but I decided to stop by since you're right on my route. Is this guy yours?"

He held up a wiggly brown puppy.

"THEO!" cried Benny.

The puppy jumped from the man's arms and ran straight to Benny. Benny hugged him tightly.

"Where did you find him?" Benny asked.

"Way on the other side of town. I saw all the signs and figured this had to be Theo. Though I offered him a lick of peanut butter ice cream just to be sure."

"Thank you so much!" said Benny.

"You're welcome!" said the ice cream man. "Would you kids like some ice cream, too?"

"Oooh—yes, please!" Benny picked peanut butter to share with Theo. Jordan chose cherry vanilla with sprinkles.

The ice cream man pulled away, tooting his horn cheerfully.

"Thanks again!" Benny called after him.

"Woof!" added Theo.

"Thank you, too, Jordan," said Benny's mom. "But how are we ever going to thank all the other people who made signs?"

"Easy," said Jordan. She grinned. "Just thank one person and ask them to thank two more. If you use doubling, you'll have a thousand thanks in no time!"